Ellen,

Omg! I did it Ellen! I am so happy to share this book with you! I pray it brings you awareness, healing and support through your own journey. I am so thankful to have you in my life. What a beautiful blessing. It was great to work with you over the years. You are a wonderful friend and supporter. Enjoy! Love you!

Always,

Poetic Healer

Poetic Healer

I Poured into Myself

Tina Cook

Also Known As

Poetic Healer

Poetic Healer

I Poured into Myself

By

Tina Cook

Also Known As

Poetic Healer

With Custom Illustrations in Color

By

Mason Porter

Creative Artistic Editing

By

Erica Brieva

Sunny's Light Enterprises, LLC, 2020

Publishing Company

United States Copyright Office

ISBN 978-1-7329989-2-6

Printed in the United States of America 2020

Poetic Healer

Poetic Healer

~About the Author~

Depleted, worn out, and stressed! A woman can experience it all at once. She can swiftly be carried away like a raft going down a river. A new plan for her life is needed immediately. Can she be saved? The journey of life can often make her feel like there is no hope. No way out! Suffocating on the lack of confidence as she attempts to pull herself up to a comfortable stance. She wants to take control of her life. Where should she begin? A quiet voice comes to her mind in a very subtle manner. It is clear and concise. "Take control, get up, you can do it." The power lies within her, but she needs to listen to her voice. In adolescence and as little girls, we are taught to act in a particular manner and seek out specific goals in life. Our voices are often stripped of us before we reach puberty. However, the yearning for growth causes a woman to be on a quest for continual discovery. The

Poetic Healer

trials and tribulations will have you reflecting and wondering how the hell you got to such a chaotic standpoint. It's okay not to be okay. The woman has to learn to understand the various pieces of herself.

The pieces of a woman make up a whole woman that is waiting to blossom like a beautiful rose. My sister pick up your pieces and reshape them if you must. Take the time to heal from the wounds of the past and present. You are important! Invest in yourself! Rediscovering your voice is a gift to yourself, and you owe it to share with the world. The world awaits the whole you. Tap into the power within! The time is now, take that first step. The new you awaits to be discovered. It will be amazing and phenomenal on the other side! See you there!

My name is Tina Cook, also known as Poetic Healer, and I am a poet and writer. I currently reside in Lawrenceville, Georgia, with my two sons, ages 18 and 12. I enjoy reading, writing, exercising, and spending time with family and friends. I started writing poetry in 2015 after being inspired by a beautiful friendship that enriched my life. The inspiration I received reminded me that loving was possible. As a result of feeling the love, I also discovered I had lovely words to share. My poetic voice was born in February 2019, and this is when I decided to write this book.

My goal is to bring poetry to life by creating short stories that support poetry pieces. Since poetry fostered my healing, I wanted to give someone that same sense of peace by sharing my poetry with the world. I have always enjoyed helping others in the human service arena. I currently have a Master's degree in Community Counseling and a Bachelor's degree in Psychology. I have worked in the healthcare industry for 18 years. My current role as a Child abuse Advocate Manager allows me the opportunity to serve one of the most vulnerable populations of children in Georgia.

Besides my current position, one of the most fulfilling ways I serve others in my community is through my women's empowerment platform "Tea with Tina" that serves as a safe space for the woman exploring self while indulging in tea, cupcakes and poetry in a relaxed and open-minded environment. Join us at "Tea with Tina" for a wonderful self-discovery experience.

~Dedication~

The depth of my heart is sincere, and my mind is overflowing with memories that helped me discover my worth. I am a woman progressing daily to be a great woman.

For my dear beautiful Grandmother, Christibell Wilson, your strength and character as a phenomenal woman gave me the power to discover myself while learning to rediscover the great woman within.

Poetic Healer

Chapters

My Life

Pathway (Poetry Piece)

When You See Me

When You See Me (Poetry Piece)

The Discovery of The Woman

Rediscover Me (Poetry Piece)

Poetic Healer

Poetic Healer

Chapter I
~My Life~

My spirit felt numb, cold, and disconnected. My soul

felt dark, gloomy, and full of distress. I wondered what I

should do next, but nothing yet came to mind. The only thing

I heard was a voice saying, "you're not a good wife, your

husband hates you, and the kids... well, the kids would just be

better off without you, so why not just end it all today?". I

already believed everyone around me would be okay without

me, so why not just go ahead and end it? I had this thought so

many times before, but that day was different. On that day, I

had an actual plan. I could've just gone and have taken all the

pills in the medicine cabinet, and it would've been over. But

then, I heard another voice within that said, "No, it is not

Poetic Healer

time, you must live!". I listened to the second voice, and I got up. My plans for that day and every day since then had changed. See, I had no clue what to do, but I knew that I was not dying on that day. Although drained, I decided to take some time out to pray. I then showered and started to clean the house.

With Darryl gone for a few days, and the girls being with my mother, it was a good time for some prayer and meditation. After all that cleaning, I went for a run in the park. That's when it all came to me. That's when I began to replay my life. I am not sure what caused me not to love Darryl anymore. Darryl and I had been married for ten years, and we had two beautiful daughters, ages eleven and eight. We had been college sweethearts, and everyone thought we were the cutest couple in our circle of friends. Little did they know, I didn't want to be with Darryl anymore.

We hadn't had sex in months, and I was just always angry with him. We were living in this shitty ass apartment, and there was no game plan to move. He hung out with his friends all the time. Even his spare time was spent with his friends.

At this point, I felt that I had no clue how to be a wife. How could I have learned how to be a wife? I came from a family of cheaters, divorcees, and drug and alcohol abusers.

I met Darryl in the bakery where I worked as a cashier. He was a transfer student at the college I attended and very new to the area. Darryl would come into the bakery shop to buy a cake for his mother. She loved the famous chocolate fudge cake made by the owner, Beverly. Beverly knew Darryl's family, and she always had beautiful things to say about him, but instead of worrying about Darryl, I was all about doing my job. I hadn't noticed Darryl the first time I saw him, but after a while, I couldn't help but to notice. He was 6'5", muscular build, and had a smile that would make any girl just melt. Let's not forget about his skin, which was a smooth peanut butter bronze tone. He had a few visible tattoos, and he looked like the type that would have a sistah staring at him all day long. I could see that he was charming, a gentleman, and I loved how he always spoke to everyone when he walked in. I thought that he was a sexy black man, but I wasn't looking for anything.

Once we locked eyes at the checkout counter, I knew he would be hard to resist. After the day at the checkout counter, we got to know each other rather quickly, and shortly after that, we decided to get married. We were married for only a year before we started having children. I had always wanted children, and being married was in the plan, so the short timeframe wasn't a factor.

I was enjoying being the mother of two beautiful baby girls. However, I was forty years old by the time I was over the idea of being a stay at home mom. Having a husband and two beautiful daughters just wasn't enough. Staying home with the girls for a few years had turned into me forfeiting my dreams of becoming a chef, and although Darryl did well at the barbershop that he owned, he had a gambling problem. Any money that he made, he wasted. I ended up having to sell baked goods here and there to help out. It was the only thing I could do since he forbade me to get a job.

I spent most of my days caring for the children, cooking, cleaning, and making sure Darryl was happy after a long day of work. It had become my routine, and there was no excitement left. Marriage is supposed to be a good thing, but I had no idea it would cause me to lose myself. How could the thought that "time isn't a factor" change to "we moved too fast" so quickly? Why couldn't I have a career, kids, and a husband simultaneously? I resented Darryl. How could I not have lost the excitement? I watched this man gamble our life away for two whole years.

At first, it was just gambling, and then he began both drinking and gambling. I tried to talk to him about it, but he was in total denial. Every time I thought about having sex with Darryl, I also thought about the fact that he was now an alcoholic. It was a turn-off mainly because I had already experienced growing up with alcoholics. I couldn't believe I was now married to one. I would have never expected all of this when we met at the bakery. I just didn't see it coming. We even got the point where we lost count of the appointments he had missed with clients. Keeping the girls away from him during one of his binges was a must.

I had to try to prevent the girls from being subjected to all the yelling and cursing. Yes, Darryl was supposed to go to the NFL. However, the injury that Darryl had sustained his junior year caused him to have to sit out for a semester. I think the damage is what started all of this with him. I did not care about the NFL. I just wanted him to be happy with our little family.

Still, Darryl blamed me for everything, including the losses on game day. I tried everything to support his dreams and even had an abortion to make sure that it wouldn't affect

Poetic Healer

his plans to be in the league, but I guess that wasn't enough. How could he have forgotten all of that? How could he forget how angry I was with having to have an abortion or how scared I was about going to get the abortion without him? I had crawled into bed after the abortion to cry and just be alone for the day, and I awoke to several missed calls.

I checked my voicemail messages, and my heart dropped at the sound of Darryl's voice, "Nicole, I am at the hospital, please come quick, I'm injured, I need you here"! I was nervous, drained, and in pain, but I jumped up and drove as fast as I could to the hospital. I was more worried about how frustrated and scared Darryl would be than I was about my own condition. He never really mentioned the abortion or asked me how I was feeling. I should have seen all the red flags right then, but of course, it was one more thing I let go. My heart ached just a little every day for months afterward. I was depressed, and I isolated myself for a while. It would be a secret I had kept over the years as I'd wonder if my baby would have been a boy or a girl.

My family did not believe in abortion. There was no way I'd tell them about what I had done. Darryl's family was not aware, either. At the time, we both were grieving a loss that no one else could empathize with since we both refused to share. It was the loss of a child and a possible future in the NFL. Over the years, we had made attempts to address those memories, hurts, and pains, but we lacked the consistency and commitment to the therapy process needed to progress.

Well, I knew that trauma had occurred in Darryl's life, but I have my childhood trauma too. The difference between Darryl's family and my family was that our family just acted as if it was reasonable to suffer from alcohol and drug abuse.

I remember being embarrassed and ashamed at times because the entire neighborhood would be aware of the shenanigans going on with my family members. I can't recall there being any interventions to help anyone of them. Often in the black community, we just deal with the fact that Uncle Ray and Cousin Pam drinks and uses drugs. Now that I see how things started with Darryl, I'm wondering what happened to Uncle Ray to cause him to start drinking.

Is Uncle Ray aware that he can get sober and healed from this illness? Well, probably not since Darryl had no clue either. Unfortunately, my girls now have the same questions that I had about their own father. I felt so bad for the girls since I wanted life to always be great for them. Since I knew to try counseling, I suggested it to Darryl. Darryl didn't care to attend counseling. He often would refuse to go. Whenever Darryl went, he would yell and scream about his football injury. He had so much anger inside, which made it difficult for me to keep being supportive. I tried to love and support Darryl through all the hardships, but everything had gotten to him, and he even began drinking throughout the week, so I decided to go to counseling by myself. My therapist felt I would benefit from it and I did. Counseling helped me to gain the clarity that I hadn't had before. I realized that I had to stop saying anything about his drinking and work on myself. I had to work on everything from my childhood experiences to the night I rushed to be by Darryl's side after having had an abortion and so much more. I called his mother and asked her to come over later that day for dinner. I prayed that Darryl would consider listening to his mother since they've always had a good relationship.

At this point, she was the only way to his heart, so when she agreed to come over, I got excited. The girls and I prepared his favorite dinner, which was salmon, mixed veggies, and cheesecake. His mother planned to be at the house around seven o'clock. The girls were so excited about Grandma Liz coming over for dinner, and Mama Liz was right on time.

It was 6:45PM when the doorbell rang. The girls ran to the door to greet Mama Liz. We all sat at the dinner table, and Darryl came downstairs to join us. Ms. Liz wasted no time; immediately after dinner was over, she asked Darryl, "how's the drinking? ". I was surprised to see that Darryl told his mom it had gotten worse. Ms. Liz explained that it was time for another intervention, and it needed to happen ASAP. I agreed but stayed quiet because I know how Darryl can be. All I could do is pray that he'd listen to his mother. This intervention was long overdue. I wanted him to go to rehab. I feel like we had lost so much time, and I had just become numb to all the chaos. I couldn't stand to see it all get worse. He agreed that he'd go to rehab by the end of the week.

I can genuinely say that it was a breath of fresh air for us all. After Ms. Liz left, Darryl told me that he has wanted to get help for some time, but he was afraid to try. When he started to tear up, I knew that he was earnest, and I just had to support him, so I hugged him. We hadn't embraced it in quite some time.

Most of Darryl's days were spent intoxicated, and I had to try to keep the girls away from him, so this hug was different for me. Darryl and I even slept in the same bed together afterward. By this time, it had been weeks since we last slept in the bed together. It felt strange but good to lay beside Darryl, especially since he hadn't had a drink that night. I reached over and hugged him again as I whispered, "we need to talk to the girls... "they're old enough and very aware of what's going on," but he remained quiet. I dozed off to sleep. In the middle of the night, I heard Darryl crying very softly on the sofa in our bedroom. I walked over to him and placed my hand on his shoulder and stood there for a while as he cried, and then I said, "Darryl, I love you and just want you to come back to the girls and me." I went back to bed and allowed him some time to gather himself.

Darryl soon came back to bed, and we both slept the entire rest of the night. I got up the next morning and cooked breakfast for the girls before they went off to school, and Darryl joined us at the table. The girls were so excited to eat breakfast with their dad. I was happy too. I had prayed for a good, sober, and peaceful day and I got just what I asked for; another quiet night again with us sleeping in the same bed together. I felt like things were normal, but I didn't want to get overly excited.

The next day, Darryl asked to have lunch with the girls at school. Our youngest Britney was looking forward to his visit, but our daughter Brandy didn't feel quite the same. When the girls were younger, Darryl had shown up to Brandy's cheer competition intoxicated, and he caused a huge scene. Brandy cried every day for a week. It was an awful experience, but I reassured Brandy that lunch with dad would be different this time.

When Brandy got home, she was so excited to tell me how great lunch had been. The atmosphere in the house was brand new and felt so good. I was sleeping better and able to focus throughout the day. The girls also appeared to be in a better mood as they got on the bus each morning. Ms. Liz called the next morning and informed me she would be driving Darryl to rehab the very next day. I wanted to go with them but instead decided that I'd stay home. I was afraid that if I went along this time, Darryl would change his mind.

We had attempted to take him so many times before, and I seemed to have been a trigger for him. One time, while on the way there, Darryl even insinuated that I might cheat on him. I had become so angry at his comment that I told him he was "a sorry excuse for a man." Then I told him to just "admit you ain't going." Ms. Liz had to calm us both down. Part of my self- care was not placing myself in positions like this again, so I knew I'd stay behind. Darryl woke up early, and I heard him leave the bedroom. I wasn't sure why he was up at 5:00 AM since Ms. Liz had planned to pick him up around 8:00 AM. I decided to go back to sleep for a bit. The girls would be up soon for school. My alarm went off at 7:00 AM, I got up and started breakfast for the girls while they showered and got ready for school, but Darryl was gone.

I searched everywhere around the house and even in the sunroom where he loves to sit and enjoy nature, but he wasn't there either. I then called his cell phone, but no answer, and his car was still in the garage. Okay, what the hell is going on, I thought. At 7:45 AM., I walked the girls to the bus stop, and they began asking me, 'Where is Daddy?" They wanted to tell him goodbye before he went off to rehab. I was worried but had to keep calm in front of the girls.

I told the girls not to worry, and everything would be fine, and I would let them know after school. I waved nervously at the girls as I walked back to the house. Ms. Liz had just pulled into our driveway. I had to tell her that Darryl was not at home. Ms. Liz immediately asked me what was going on. I told her that at around 5:00 AM. Darryl got up and left the bedroom. I had assumed he was just getting up to prepare to leave for rehab, but he was gone.

Ms. Liz and I both were now officially worried. Had Darryl decided not to go to rehab? My heart was pounding because I wasn't sure where to look for Darryl. He had so many spots he would retreat to when he went on his drinking binges, and he would be there for days. I had to pray to God that this wasn't the case. Ms. Liz called his brothers and uncles for help, but no one had heard from him. I left Darryl a third voicemail message, begging him to call his mother and I. An hour had almost passed, and still no sign of Darryl. It was so stressful to be in the middle of this ordeal.

I just wanted to believe in him and even cheer him on, but here I was having second thoughts. After about three hours, Darryl called his mother's phone. Darryl admitted he had been drinking, but he still wanted to go to rehab. Ms. Liz tried not to cry, but I could see her eyes filling up with tears.

She asked Darryl if we could come to pick him up, and he
agreed. We called the rehab center to see if his spot was still
available and thanked God that it was, but we'd have to make
it there within two hours or else. Even though my nerves
were a wreck, I told Ms. Liz, I would go with her to pick up
Darryl. Come to find out; he had gone to the local cemetery
where his father had laid to rest. Darryl's father had died of a
heart attack when he was sixteen years old.

Honestly, I knew that Darryl suffered some
significant losses. I accepted that it was time for us both to
heal but sheesh. We picked Darryl up, and he started to tear
up. We hugged him and went on our way to the rehab center.
It was good to know that I'd be able to focus on myself and
the girls for a while. It was also good to see that he was
getting the help he needed. Here it was, three months later,
and Darryl had completed his time at the rehab center.

After rehab, we went back to living as usual, but this
time Darryl had been sober for six months. I awakened every

day with gratitude in my heart, and I prayed that Darryl
would never go back. It was a sunny day in March, and
Darryl had gone back to work at the barbershop. I had started
working part-time at the local bakery again. We were all
attending therapy, and the girls were happier now, but then it
all came to a halt when I checked the mail. Darryl hadn't paid
the mortgage in about six months. I thought he had it handled
while he was in rehab, and especially after he got back since
he was at the barbershop again, but I guess not. I mean, he
was sober and went to work every day. Where is the money
going? The barbershop business appeared to be doing well,
so why did this happen? When I confronted Darryl, he just
grabbed the letter and walked away from me.

Here we go again, I thought. Things were looking up,
but now we're back to this. What am I supposed to do? The
house was ready to be in foreclosure, and Darryl finally
admitted that we had no money. He had been gambling
again. He even sold the barbershop. I just started crying, and

then the anger settled in, so I yelled, "Darryl, I can't do this anymore! We are about to lose our home, and it's all your fault!". With tears running down my face, I started packing my clothes.

I couldn't help to think that I was glad the girls were away at my mother's for spring break. I planned to get them at the end of the week. Darryl tried to stop me from leaving, but I kept it moving. Before I left, he told me he had a drink earlier, and he felt awful. I couldn't bring myself to feel anything for him. I got in the car and sped away to Monica's place. I cried the entire way to Monica's. Then when I got to Monica's, I called Ms. Liz and told her I couldn't stay with Darryl any longer. She begged me to calm down and reconsider, but there was no coming back from this. I couldn't spend another night in that house. I was aware that I had not always been the most supportive wife, and I still had some healing to do, but I was tired with no more to give.

Darryl pretty much called me all night until my voicemail wouldn't take any more messages. The next day I reached out to him and asked him to give me some space and that I'd call him when I was ready to talk. I had never envisioned my life to be in shambles like this. I wanted the perfect life but ended up with this. It was far from perfect, and I was hurt, but I knew there had to be a better way. I called Darryl two days later and asked him to meet me at the nearby coffee shop. He begged me to come home, but I refused. Our talk ended up being almost two hours long. I let all my feelings out and told him I loved him, but I couldn't possibly be sure about what was supposed to be next. I apologized to Darryl for yelling and screaming at him.

I wanted to be different, I wanted the healed and full version of Darryl to show up, and when he didn't show up the way I'd hoped, my disappointment grew. He admitted that it was hard to talk to me at times whenever I had been judgmental over the years, and I confessed to him that I had thought to end my life at one point. I couldn't believe I was admitting this out loud, but he needed to know just how bad it all affected me.

The chaos of alcohol and gambling had consumed his entire adult life. The trauma from it all consumed mine. He asked me if we could move and start over again, and I wondered if he could try to heal from all the open wounds. We had bought a home and lost it. What would we be going back to anyways? Our Pathway had been so rocky from the beginning. I prayed and meditated for a few days while my mother kept the girls so I could try to figure things out. During that time, Darryl and I would also meet at the park to talk and to try and decide if we could continue our lives together.

After about a month, we concluded we would work to rebuild our lives and start over. The couples counseling we'd started going to over the past month had helped us look within and discover opportunities we both needed to adhere to in order to heal and be whole. We moved into a new apartment together, and we got the girls involved in family counseling nearby.

I later opened a bakery shop, and a year after, Darryl started a barber school. He was working on developing a program for young male athletes that wanted to pursue college and play at the collegiate level. I was so glad to see that he could use his NFL training to help the young men that he mentored. I saw a whole new man that was thriving now. We were doing the work together, and we knew we had finally chosen each other. The weight of all our past issues no longer had control of us. We were in control, and our life was better than ever. Things weren't at the endpoint, but now it's as perfect as can be. Even with the flaws, we've come to see that we're perfect for each other. Letting go of the whirlwind that my life had been and starting over was the best decision ever. Who would've thought I'd take another chance, but I did, and I don't regret anything.

Poetic Healer

Our days were now more relaxed because we vowed to work at it daily. I was so proud to see that we didn't give up on each other. We got back to being happily married and enjoyed the girls as they embraced becoming teenagers. Our lives would never be the same going forward . We wanted to be a living example to our daughters and our community that "Black Love" exists, and it does because here we are, together again on this pathway.

The Pathway

The Pathway of life often varies. The path may be
smooth, while at times it may be rocky and full of pebbles,
rocks, and particles that get in our way.

While it is essential to move forward and conquer the
path, take notice of the rocky road. Notice the shape and size
of the rocks. How does it affect your life? What purpose does
it serve? How can you use it? Can you offer it to others? Can
you share your testimony?

I have learned not merely to step over or push the

rocks and pebbles away. I now stop and pick them up. I make

a note of where they are on my path and how it serves my

life. I savor in the path, smooth or rocky.

Life has a way of changing quite often. Savor each

moment. Remember each significant pebble or stone on your

path.

It will tell the story.

Chapter II
~When You See Me~

I looked in the mirror, and I could see that my right

eye was wounded and closed shut. My lips were puffed up,

bright red, and I could see that both my top and bottom lip

were busted. My hair was in disarray, and my neck hurt so

badly that I could barely turn my head. I could even see a

significant red mark around my neck, almost like handprints.

My abuser had punched and choked me. As I continued to

stare into the mirror, I also saw a lost and scared woman

looking back at me. "Where had my life gone wrong? When

did it happen, and How the hell did I get here?".

Standing in the mirror battered and bruised, I had no

clue what to do next. I just always thought I was too smart

and knew better, but here I am, unable to recognize myself.

Poetic Healer

Todd was my boyfriend. I think this was like the tenth time Todd had hit me. I had lost count after the third time. I did not want anyone to see me like this. I was so ashamed, and I felt terrible, so I did what I knew how to do best. I didn't go to work. I called my job and told my supervisor I was sick. I then crawled back into bed and cried my heart out. I stayed in bed all day wondering how or if I'd ever be able to escape the pain. I did not want my family or friends to know anything, and so I endured each of his abusive episodes alone. The bruises were extremely severe this time, and Todd was in the kind of rage that showed me no mercy.

I was exhausted from crying so much that I slept most of the day. I cried so much that my face felt like sandpaper. At this point, it was six o'clock in the evening. Although I had put my phone on do not disturb, I had twenty missed calls and a dozen text messages.

Instead of returning the calls, I decided to isolate myself and take the next couple days off while Todd would

be away just to figure out what next step would be best. Todd
and I had been together for five years. We had been living
together for about a year. His violent rages started about two
years ago while we were dating. It was a beautiful summer
day in Atlanta. Downtown Atlanta was gorgeous in the
summer months so we decided to head to the city for the day.
Positive vibes filled the air as we walked on Peachtree Street,
enjoying the scenery. We simply enjoyed each other's
company, so we didn't need much to laugh together. "People
watching" was our thing. To me, Todd was a relaxed and
laid-back kind of guy. He was 5'10, dark, had smooth skin
with a smile so bright that he could light a room. On this day,
something different happened. As we headed to the car, a guy
in passing who appeared intoxicated winked at me. Todd
became protective and asked the guy to please step back as
he approached me. The guy began to get loud with Todd,
"Oh is that your girl? she's beautiful man," the guy said. Todd
warned the guy to go on, and he did. Afterward, Todd

proceeded to tell me how he did not like the guy approaching us.

I told Todd not to worry about the guy because the guy looked drunk. Todd said he did not care and blamed it all on my outfit. I thought, "hmmm, my outfit?". I only had on a yellow short maxi sundress and camel color sandals, which I thought was cute and appropriate for our night on the town, but I guess Todd didn't feel the same. I told Todd I thought he was overreacting and that he needed to just relax. However, Todd continued his rant. I had never seen him react in this manner before to something like this. He told me I was probably dressing like this to get attention from other guys. I calmly said to him that I loved him and that I would never wear something to disrespect him intentionally, but it didn't help. Todd continued his rant even more, and when we got to the car, Todd yelled, "YOU ARE A BITCH." Todd then slapped me several times while yelling and telling me never to disrespect him again.

"You better shape up quick," Todd said. I tried to talk, and as I started to speak, he slapped me again. At that point, I decided to just be silent.

The car ride home was very stressful and all I could think about is what this man just did to me. This loving man that I have been with instantly turned into a monster. My heart pounded so hard as he pulled the car into the driveway. I was so fearful of going inside with him considering what he had just done to me outdoors. I imagined things being so much worse indoors. Once he parked, he yelled, "GET OUT OF THE CAR RIGHT NOW, BITCH." I quickly got out of the car, and I went into the house. I tried not to act as if I was afraid, but I can't ever recall a time when I had been so scared.

Todd told me to go clean up and that we will go to dinner later. I went to the bedroom, sat on the edge of the bed, and I cried my heart out yet again. Soon Todd joined me in the bedroom, and he proceeded to tell me how much he loved me, Todd apologized and told me how he would never hit me again. Todd also explained to me that he had gotten angry, felt very jealous, and his temper just got the best of him. So later that night, we went to dinner, and we never brought it up again, but I was still afraid. The next day I decided to go for a jog in the park. I'm glad I had requested the day off previously, and since Todd had left, it was a perfect time. The day off was right on time, mainly because it gave me room to think about what happened the day before. I tried to think back to the beginning of our relationship as I asked myself if I had seen any signs that he would've done this, and I did, but I ignored them all. Todd and I had bought a house near the downtown Atlanta area.

Now that I think about it, Todd had made all the decisions. He made decisions about where we lived, the kind of car I drove, the friends I had except one, my hair cut and color. OMG, he has been controlling me! I wanted to cry.

I took a big swallow to try to remove that piercing force in my throat. I held back the tears, but my life was a mess.

I needed to get out of this warzone but I was too embarrassed to talk with anyone about this, so I kept it to myself. No one knew, not my friends, not my family, no one. After all, everyone would just think that I was weak, and they'd just tell me to walk the hell out. But I loved Todd, and I wanted to be with him. Leaving was not an option. There had to be something I could do to make things right.

I could not understand why a gentleman like Todd would hurt me. I started to think about leaving but then wondered where I could go that Todd wouldn't find me. There was nowhere. He knew what all my options were. My head started to throb, and I had enough. I could not spend another minute thinking about all the pain that I had experienced, so I got up and decided to watch TV and to make myself some dinner. I cannot believe I am in this mess,

I said. I've got to snap out of this shit! I am too smart for this! I have a college degree, came from a two-parent household. I've got my life together. NOT!

Well, at least at one point, I thought I had my life together. I feel awful inside, and now I look horrible on the outside! My heart is pounding, and I'm sweating. OMG! What is wrong with me? I think I am coming on with a panic attack. I ran to the bedroom to try and lie down. However, I tripped over my shoe and fell to the floor. The room was closing in on me. I tried to yell for help, but no one could hear me. Lying on the floor, terrified with tears rolling down my face, I just began to pray, "God, please help me." Several hours passed by, and when I woke up, it was dark outside. I felt so sluggish. I checked my phone, and by this time, Todd had called me ten times. My heart started to pound hard all over again. Todd left me several long messages. I decided just to call him and go through it. The phone barely rang one time "Hey, Trisha, why the hell you not answering your phone?", Todd asked. I told him I hadn't felt well, so I went to sleep. He asked me if I had been out of the house, and that's when I told him I missed work.

I probably cannot go tomorrow either because of my swollen face, I said. Todd told me he would give me the money for my missed days of work, but of course, I did not care about the money. I wanted my life. "You better not think about leaving, and nobody else wants you anyway," Todd threatened. I was starting to think I might be trapped forever. At this point, I was so tired of lying to everyone about being sick, and tired of saying I forgot about their engagements.

I have not been home to Mississippi in years. My family thinks I am a workaholic, and I just cannot come back, but the truth is that I'm hiding the scars. My father would kill Todd if he knew, but I can't tell him either. The panic attacks are getting worse, and I've reached my limit on missing days at work. I figured I'd try to stay away from Todd as much as possible so he will not have an opportunity to hit me, but of

course, I knew that he would because he was Todd. My alarm
went off, and it was 6 AM. I was still exhausted and not sure
if I could even get up. I jumped up to go to the bathroom, and
I looked in the mirror. Face slightly still swollen, and lip
busted. Shit! I need to go to work, I needed to get out of this
house, so I put on some makeup and left. Maybe I could hang
out with my girl Jennifer. I called her Jenny.

Jenny was a successful real estate attorney who lived
in midtown, and we had been friends since our college days.
Jenny was a relaxed and laid-back chick, so pretty, and so
strong. Her long black hair was thick and curly. Jenny grew
up in Alabama, and she was very popular with the men.
Although she was single, she had no desire to be in a
relationship. Jenny's thing was, "black men play too many
games." Jenny would say that she just might settle down with
a white guy. Jenny did not care what the black community
had to say about her being in an interracial relationship since
she was always going to do what made her happy. If I tell

Jenny what's been happening, it's over for Todd, especially because Jenny did not like Todd. Whenever she would come around, she would say to me that he seemed cold, distant, and detached.

In the past, I had always made excuses for his odd behavior. I even attempted to tell Jenny how loving Todd had been in the beginning, but Jenny always would say, "Well, he isn't like that now." I arrived in the parking lot at precisely 7:45 AM after stopping at the nearby cafe for a tall blonde. Our morning meeting starts at 8:00 AM, and I had to put my game face on. "Jesus take the wheel, please get me through this," I said. I walked in, and people immediately asked how I was feeling. I smiled and responded, "I'm okay. Thanks for asking." Right as they were asking, Todd texted me and reminded me to act normal or else. My heart started to beat fast.

Oh My God! No, I cannot have a panic attack at the office. I walked quickly to the bathroom and went into the first stall I could see. I locked the door and put my head between my legs. I took a few deep breaths, and I started to feel better. I told myself, "Trisha, get it together; all you have is this job, so smile and get your ass to the morning meeting." I walked out of the bathroom like a BOSS! Who the hell was I fooling? I am not a BOSS! I am living with a man that beats me every week, and I am almost sure he is cheating on me.

Nevertheless, I made it through the day. I called Jenny and asked could we go to dinner and drinks. I was so glad that Jenny was down to meet me. We had not seen each other in about a month but I had to try and stay away because the beatings were getting worse. I was not sure what Jenny would say if she knew the truth, and I wasn't a fan of being shamed.

All I know is that most women would not stay in a situation like that, but I was one of the ones who just did not know how to leave. Todd had convinced me to isolate myself even more. His jealousy and paranoia were taking over. I

Poetic Healer

prayed to God to give me a plan to help myself and waited as patiently as I could. I headed to the restaurant to meet Jenny. Incoming call. DAMN! It was Todd. I answered, and he immediately started up by saying he would be home tomorrow morning, and that I better come straight back from work.

All I could say was, "Okay, Dear." Todd asked me about my whereabouts and the condition of my face. I told him I was headed to a quick dinner with Jenny, and my face was not as swollen as before. I'm guessing that he only asked because I texted him a picture of myself asking him for a reason as to why he did this to me. Of course, he replied with the same lame-ass excuse, he did not mean to do it. He then said I needed to listen to him, and that I should just not cause any more problems. Todd then promised to buy me a new diamond necklace and take me on a trip to Italy. He was great about gift-giving, but I had grown to be tired of all that. I only needed a plan to escape. I only wanted to live and be free of all the violence. I was aware of agencies that helped women with domestic violence issues, but the embarrassment kept me away from those places. I did not want to go to a shelter and so none of the real options were good options for me.

I knew if I tried to leave Todd, he would find me and kill me. I had some money saved up, but I was so afraid to leave that the money didn't matter. I mean, where would I go? How could I start over? I asked myself.

Jenny was waiting at the bar for me, and she had ordered my usual vodka and cranberry juice. We chatted and caught up. I told Jenny all about work and how I had been sick and needed a vacation. Jenny knew something was up. She looked at me and said. "Trisha, you don't look your best girl, what the hell is going on, I have not seen you in a month, you avoid me and only text me, sis, what is going on?". I told Jenny that I would be fine but she did not believe my story. I tried so hard just to seem mentally healthy, but when she asked me about how Todd and I were doing, my heart started to race.

As Jenny continued to say his name, I could hardly speak. She reached out to touch my shoulder, and I pulled back quickly and yelled, "Ouch!". Todd had slammed my shoulder into the wall while I was trying to get away from him. Jenny promptly asked me what was wrong.

My eyes began to water, and tears ran down my face uncontrollably. I tried to stop, but I could not stop crying. Jenny grabbed me and hugged me. She begged me to talk, but I couldn't. Jenny paid for the check and told me to go to her car so that we could talk. I followed her as she kept me close to her. We sat in her car, and I wiped my face with the napkin she had given me. As I wiped my lips, I also exposed the busted lip Todd had given me. "OH MY GOD TRISHA, YOUR LIP," said Jenny. I tried to hold back the tears, but I could not. It's at that point, I told her Todd did it, and he has been beating me for about two years. Jenny immediately

Poetic Healer

started to cuss, and she yelled so loud the person passing by was startled. Jenny held my hand, and she touched my face with her other hand. When Jenny started to cry with me, I knew it was worse than I thought and that I had to do something about it. Jenny confessed to me that her college boyfriend Dontae had hit her one time, and that is why she broke up with him. I had no idea Jenny went through that with Dontae, but it was good to have a friend who not only understood but also dared to leave.

I knew she would be there for me through this. She told me she would help me leave Todd, and I had to pack up "ASAP." I confessed to everything that had happened with Todd. I told her I had lost myself and was not sure who I was anymore. I explained to her that with having people see me as this successful woman with a great life, it made it that much harder to leave. I didn't want my perfect image shattered. However, I was miserable and fearful. I hated being an accountant, but I was used to living the life that everyone else expected me to live. My new start would be my dream of living in a smaller city where I could have a garden since I missed the hometown feeling of my home in Mississippi. I wanted peace, but Todd wanted status. No more trips, purses, clothes, shoes, and jewelry, and I would be okay with that if the violence stopped.

Once we were in the car, Jenny told me I could come to her house for the night, and she would help me with a plan. Right then, I realized that God had answered my prayers. I knew I would have to end all communication with Todd, and I could not look back. I was ready for a new life.

I got into my car, and Jenny followed me to my house. I packed my bags and anything of significant value, I called my boss and explained that I needed a leave of absence, and I told him that I would be in touch tomorrow morning as I continued packing. Todd texted me while I was packing, and I almost didn't answer, but Jenny suggested I respond just as I usually would, and so I did. So many things went through my mind as I walked around the house to gather my belongings. I deleted all my accounts on social media, emails, and had Jenny take photographs of significant telephone numbers for me. I wiped my phone clean and removed all data, and then broke the phone into pieces. I held onto the broken phone because I was looking forward to throwing it in the trash at Jenny's house. My dad found out and was devastated. He bought me a plane ticket for the next day to arrive in Mississippi. I was so ashamed because I wanted my family and friends to see me as a strong woman, but Jenny reminded me that I'd done a beautiful thing by confessing the truth and for leaving.

Jenny agreed to fly to my parents' house with me. When I arrived at Jenny's house, I took a hot shower and had a glass of wine. I finished telling her all about the panic attacks. I also forwarded Jenny all the pictures of the bruises that I had over the last year. Jenny tried not to cry, but she could not help it.

Together we decided to go ahead and report it to the police, and so I called the local police and filed a report. Afterward, I went to bed. I had not slept that well in months. Jenny stayed close by and reassured me all would be well. I knew I had a long road ahead of me, but I had to leave and make a better life for myself.

The next morning, I woke up, and it felt strange because I started to feel a sense of peace. I would purchase a new phone once I got to my parent's house and begin to figure it all out. The plane ride was quiet. I cried and held Jenny's hand tightly, and I prayed for the first time in a while. It had been months since I last prayed.

I was afraid that Todd might find me or try to hurt my family. My family reassured me we all would be fine. After I arrived home, the next few days were a blur. Jenny stayed for three days, and my family ensured I was safe. It was challenging to explain everything to the rest of my family. I had so much guilt and shame, but thankfully they were supportive and nonjudgmental. Well, everyone except my sister. She just ranted and raved about how crazy I must be and how she would never live like that. It was so upsetting to hear my sister speak to me like that, but I had to stay focused. I must mute the noise, go on a search within, and allow Trisha to heal, I said to myself. It has been a long time since I sat quietly to hear myself think and even breathe. I started on my search by going for my walk down by the lake near my parents' home. I felt so at peace. I found out that Todd had been reaching out to family members and friends. Jenny even told me he called her yelling and screaming, but she hung upon him. He became desperate and attempted to come to her house, but her new boyfriend met him at the door. I still got nervous at times, but therapy helps. I had begun to address my self-esteem issues, and each day started to get better and better. A few months passed, and I got a call from the local police in Atlanta. It had appeared I would have to testify if

Todd decided to take the case to trial. My heart started racing all over again.

I felt a bit afraid to face all of this, but my family and close friends reminded me how far I had come and told me that it would all be okay in due time. The empathy that my family showed me gave me some comfort and strength to deal with everything. One of the great things about all of this is that Todd and I hadn't gotten married, and we had no children together. It would've been so much harder to break away had those things been a part of what we had.

These changes reminded me that I still had my life to live. I now had hope. Within was a belief that I could continue to heal and be a light for so many other women. I want others to know that although the pain I felt was awful, healing is possible. Although the inner scars will take a lot longer to heal, my physical injuries have begun to heal. I am healing daily. Life is starting over and with a new accounting business right here in Mississippi. I plan to take it slow and wait to see if I will have to go back to Atlanta.

After all, it wouldn't be so bad with Jenny there with me, but I'm figuring it out. I appreciate Jenny so much. I am grateful for everything from the frequent visits to the dinner and drinks that began this journey to freedom. I may never have gotten the courage to talk with her about this, but she provided a safe space that genuinely helped me to share. Todd got arrested a few months after I left Atlanta. He chose to go to trial, so of course, I had to be "alright" and deal with facing my abuser. I knew I had to testify. Todd needed to understand that his behavior was unacceptable. The prosecutor was helpful and the team prepared me for the trial, so the nerves weren't as bad as they could've been. Before the trial began, I learned that Todd had physically assaulted a girlfriend in high school, and she was also willing to testify. It was sad to know this had happened to another woman. He certainly was a troubled person. Even though I was there to testify against him, I prayed for Todd because I had forgiven

him. I had to forgive him for myself. The anger I felt was

holding me back, and the anxiety had been extremely

overwhelming. I had to release the old to embrace the new. I

entered the courtroom, ready to testify. I did not want to

make eye contact with Todd, but it was hard not to. The

encounters from over the last two years were still very fresh

in my mind.

Besides, I had to identify him and point him out in the

courtroom. I prayed as I pointed at him. "God, please keep

me steadfast at this moment". Todd has lost weight, and he

barely wanted to look at me.

I could see he was trying to act tough, but I knew him

well enough to know that he was far from that. Oh well, I

said to myself. I held my head high and told the Judge

everything. It was difficult at times to relive the scenarios,

but I had to. This process was bigger than me. I had to do it

both for myself as well as others. As I spoke, I also thought about my last therapy session and my close friend Sherry whom I had lost in my early twenties. I think I had blocked it out of my memory due to the deep pain it caused. Sherry died at the hands of her boyfriend shortly after I had moved to Atlanta. I had no idea she was in a domestic violence situation because we lost touch when I moved away. Sherry was a beautiful person who was full of life. Her smile was as big as the rays of the sun on the sunniest day.

Sherry confessed in our last conversation right before I left for Atlanta that she recently had a miscarriage and was hoping to try to go back to college. We all knew that Sherry had a live-in boyfriend, but we had no clue she was going through so much. Out of nowhere, I got a call one day that Sherry had died as a result of her boyfriend brutally hurting her. The police had found Sherry's body in their apartment, and Sherry had been stabbed thirteen times by her accuser. The police told me it was self-defense, but I knew otherwise. They later found letters Sherry had written. The letters revealed that her boyfriend had been beating her for about six months, and he had told her that she would be dead if she ever thought about leaving him. Sherry never mentioned the brutal beatings that she described in those letters during our few conversations.

As I sat in the courtroom, I began crying because I can imagine how Sherry must have felt. When I stepped down off the stand, I felt thankful and liberated. "I made it through Sherry, and this is for us!" I said. My family ran up to me in the hallway and hugged me. It finally was over, and now we await the court's decision.

Jenny smiled at me and reminded me that I was a beautiful soul. I thanked her for loving me and being such a lovely friend. We all need a Jenny or two in our lives. She truly is a fantastic soul herself. Her love is unconditional, she is nonjudgmental, and she is real.

The verdict was back, and the Judge said, "guilty." Todd was charged with fifteen years and was in shock. His family was present in the courtroom. They, too, were in shock and there were a few outbursts made from the family. I could understand why. After all, they loved him, and I'm sure they wouldn't have wanted this for him. I took a deep breath, and as I exhaled, I realized that I could finally close this chapter in my life. It was time to rewrite my story the way I wanted it written.

My first chapter would be where I stood tall and became a woman of courage and resiliency. I had found a local Domestic violence shelter to volunteer at in Mississippi, and it felt good to go and share my story with the women at the shelter. I felt freer than ever, as I shared. My family was now living close by, and I was slowly putting my life back together piece by piece. I had made so much progress, and there had been a lot of growth.

I wanted people to see me for the new me, and it was beautiful to see that happening. My heart goes out to any woman or man that has been in a domestic violence encounter. After the ordeal, I was mindful to advise anyone I met going through abusive relationships to get help and reminded them that they weren't alone. It became a mission for me to educate and empower others just as I had been. I am thinking about visiting Jenny in Atlanta in the next few weeks. I love how often we talk, but I am looking forward to our girl's trip for the summer. I love the beach, and I'm ready! I have been in the gym these last few months trying to get prepared. I told Jenny she better be ready. We are going to be boss ladies on the beach! I can't wait to tell her about the guy I met at the gym. He's kind and polite, but I'm not rushing into anything. Only leaving myself open to whatever is next.

In the meantime, I'll keep loving myself and enjoying my journey. Maybe I'll start writing a book about my life, who knows?! Jenny loved the idea of me writing a book. I believe my story can make a difference and help other

women. Oh yeah, I planted that garden in my new back yard.

I can't wait to pick my fruits and vegetables. I just go and sit

on my back porch and admire my cute little garden. I love it.

My dad comes over often and helps me keep it in

order. He tends to give me hope that I will experience love in

my lifetime, but watching my garden grow is good enough

for me right now. I am thankful for the love and support of

family as I continue my journey. Today, I planted a new tree

in my yard in honor of Sherry. I placed a purple ribbon on it

since purple was our favorite color. I love her and miss her so

much, but I know that she is watching me from afar and we

shall meet again. Despite it all, I pray that Todd finds peace

while he is in jail. Forgiveness was now a great friend to me,

and I could only hope that mercy and peace will become a

friend to him as well.

When You See Me

When you see me, I hope one can see I have an inner core that is gentle and meek. My exterior is excellent, vibrant and built for resiliency. Yet I often have fears and worries just like every other person.

When you see me, I hope one can see I am a proud mother, sister, daughter, and friend. I strive to be kind and love others daily. I am imperfect, willing to be open to an abundance of knowledge from those around me.

When you see me, I want you to know I often sit in silence and think about how my life's progress will occur. What's next?

When you see me, I want you to know I love the quiet days I experienced while visiting my grandparents in the country. Lots of trees, flowers, and life was a lot slower, and I could always reflect and find peace.

When you see me, I want you to know my heart is filled with joy through music, reading, and watching those special to me live life with no regrets. I continue to search for ways to continue to experience peace and joy daily.

When you see me, I want you to know I cry and feel sadness too. I am a human vessel on a journey that will continue to pursue happiness. When my days filled with stress and hardship, I go to my private place.

Silence. Solace moment to hear my inner voice speak to me. I am a private person often misunderstood by others.

Some may say I am rigid and unapproachable. I am commonly known not to get close to others quickly.

I must allow time and experiences to play out. I am a quiet soul continuing to reach for the highest achievement. To continue to love myself so that I can love others.

Chapter III
~The Discovery of the Woman~

Her eyes filled with tears; she felt broken inside. It was time to rebuild her foundation all over again. Newly divorced, and for the second time, she was working on figuring out how to be the woman God created her to be. Everyone she met would tell her that she was sweet, kind, and reliable. However, these days, Lisa didn't believe any of those things about herself. Her second marriage had begun and ended so quickly. The unhealed pain and distress she experienced over the years had taken its course, and ultimately being kind made her resentful and passive-aggressive. It was like her soul was absent from her heart and her heart ached for a life that she felt was owed to her.

Poetic Healer

It was time to heal from past wounds; it was time to "feel" the pain for once. No more masking, no more avoiding the truth, it was time to rediscover her true authentic self. In recent years, an excellent dear friend told her, "Lisa, you must feel to heal," and so she braced herself for the ride to rediscovery. First, Lisa remembered being a young girl who always wanted to be married and have children. Her desire to be a wife and to love a man unconditionally had not been at the forefront of her mind.

Her perception that marriage based on past teaching was that marriage should be on her list of priorities. She also had been taught that her list of priorities should begin with graduating from high school, going to college, getting a good education, and then getting married.

Here she was 35 years old and rebuilding life all over again as if this list of priorities hadn't ever been set. She couldn't recall when it all began, nor could she remember when she lost her way. Maybe it was before she got married the first time, or perhaps it was because she had experienced

her parents' divorce when she was a teenager. Perhaps it was

a culmination of all the traumatic experiences encountered

over the short span of her lifetime. Either way, it happened,

and she was adjusting to it all. Lisa was once again getting

used to being categorized as a new divorcee and a single

parent of two beautiful children. The only difference between

this time and the last time was that her sense of self-

awareness helped her to realize that she had found her voice.

Lisa needed to heal from all the open wounds that hadn't

improved over the years. She began to pray more to release

her burdens. As she acknowledged her truth, Lisa also

embraced that it was okay not to be "okay." This

understanding is what gave her the power to begin healing,

renewing, and rebuilding her life again.

Her discovery of meditation, prayer, exercise, and the

ability to honor her voice was liberating. She would utilize

these self-care methods regularly. Each day, she strived to be better than the day before. As she sat on the couch in her home with no husband, two children, and barely enough money to pay for all her expenses, she wept. Although she'd begun prayer, meditation, and a host of other self-care routines, she still questioned if she could ever feel whole. There was a lingering void that just wouldn't go away.

Lisa had experienced a childhood around strong women, so having all these questions and feelings that were bringing her down was bizarre to her. "I'm fearfully and wonderfully made," so how'd I end up alone? She asked. The women in her family lead with a tremendous amount of resilience to withstand obstacles and stressors of life. How is it that I am here with absolutely no clue as to how to be the woman that they are, she asked. It's a terrible situation in which to find yourself. But then Lisa had an epiphany that answered her questions. The reason that the women were the way that they were was partly that the men were often secondary to the women.

Having had experiences in adolescence with her father, grandfathers, uncles, and male cousins, she now realized the stories created that were often through the lenses of the women and there lies some of her imbalance. Emotional intelligence was not of great importance to the men and women in Lisa's life as a child, and it showed. This imbalance is what had left her with the voids that she felt. The imbalance, unfortunately, also manifested itself in her marriages and her inability to connect. In addition to her self-care routines, Lisa decided to go to therapy. She called the EAP services and found a local therapist. Within a few days, therapy sessions began. It was odd at first mainly because she had chosen to see an older white male therapist.

She wasn't sure if he would be able to relate or empathize since she was a black female. However, after the first session, she was pleasantly surprised to see how open and helpful the therapist was to her. Lisa was candid in her conversation with the therapist. She described how she had masked her feelings for the last three to four years and explained that she just wanted to feel alive again. As she told her story about her ex-husband's affair, she began to recall all the reasons she had lost respect for him. It was such an awkward conversation, and of course, talking about how her marriage had ended wasn't the most fun thing to do. It was quite embarrassing, but Lisa pushed through and allowed herself to endure all the phases of her healing process, which included grieving and learning to love herself. One of the very first steps of her journey included being present. She was learning to love every part of herself, including the good, the bad, and the ugly. The grieving portion of her journey to healing and the loss of the relationship was one of the most challenging things to have embraced, but she grew more robust over time. Therapy gave her hope. She found the once shattered voice in the stories of guilt, shame, and fear. It was just what she needed.

The more Lisa attended therapy, the more she started

to envision an even stronger and wiser version of herself. She

wrote in her journal daily and started to feel more

comfortable talking with her close friends about her journey.

It was liberating to remove the negative memories and the

depiction of failure from her mind.

You would think that once the mental and emotional

state had improved, it would have solved everything else, but

it didn't. Healing wasn't the only thing that Lisa had to work

towards getting to. In addition to rebuilding her life

emotionally and mentally, Lisa had to work on getting things

together financially. Lisa wanted to make sure she took great

care of her children, the promotion at work helped a bit, but

the financial aspect of the journey was still hard. What Lisa

came to realize is that requesting and accepting support was

better than the isolation and sacrifice she had been used to

experiencing. The safety in isolation had no longer felt like a

safe space. The realization that trying to do it alone wasn't the answer became an answer. The new tribe that Lisa enlisted consisted of women that were non-judgmental, loving, and had a strong sense of sisterhood. The relationship with her new tribe helped her in so many ways. The shame she endured made facing her family unbearable. Hence, the reason she only visited every few years, but with this new-found life and new sisterhood, she felt more comfortable with the idea of inviting her family back into her life again. Therapy ended, and it was time to figure out how to continue holding herself accountable. With more methods added to the journey to health, wellness, and self-love, the new life continued. The 10-week online accountability course with one of the most fierce and outgoing leaders she had registered for added to her personal growth even more.

Lisa remembers the first assignment, which was a love letter to her younger self. As she sat down to write herself a love letter, she thought about herself as a little girl and what she would want to say to the little girl now as an adult. The message within the letter was incredibly intimate and reminded the little girl within her to let go and to love herself. This letter was simply liberating.

"Dear Lisa,

The time has come for me to tell you that It's Okay. It's okay not to be okay. Be strong, stay motivated, and remain committed. I love you. Don't listen to the voices of the world. Discover your voice. Love yourself, Dear, and you'll be able to love others. When you feel afraid, it's okay to remember your power and look up to the hills. Pray for you to know that this is where your help comes from. When you have those lonely nights, just remember that God is with you. Trust yourself just a little bit more each day. You are a mighty stable vessel, and God loves you".

As Lisa read the letter aloud, she began to feel the voids within being filled. Lisa knew that the prayers, as well as the work she had done towards her healing, was paying off. Self-love turned into self-discovery as Lisa began to examine the details of her thought processes. This new beginning was just what she needed. Lisa had spent so much time being everything to everyone else, so spending time with herself made perfect sense. She would ask herself questions like "who am I, what is my favorite food, what do I like to do for fun, what is my least favorite activity, and what is my most favorite thing to do? She found so much enjoyment in making the list that she even laughed as she discovered so many great things about herself. It was like heaven getting to know her new self. It was the best gift she'd ever given herself, Self-love! Lisa loved the letter and her new-found sense of self so much that it inspired her to start a new journal entry entitled "I am a new woman."

Lisa would enjoy hot tea while she wrote in her journal. She felt alive and free as she wrote her journal entry. The tea made her writing relaxing and comforting. Lisa became dedicated to her goal which was to live life on purpose. The notion of giving up was no longer an option.

As Lisa was embracing her new life, she then discovered a new life of expression. Lisa also found her love to speak. Lisa now had a voice to go along with her life experiences. Becoming a motivational speaker had become a new path for Lisa's life. Over the next few months, Lisa continued moving forward on her journey by researching successful speakers, continuing therapy, hiring a life coach, and creating a plan for future speaking engagements. Lisa was amazed at the beautiful people she had started to meet. Her life was slowly and positively gaining momentum. She knew that giving her story a voice would help others along their pathway. Since Lisa was no longer ashamed to attend therapy or ashamed of being divorced twice, she was ready.

Lisa had motivational speaking- engagements scheduled for the upcoming year, and was super excited.

The children were now doing great both at home and at school. Her co-parenting experiences remained on track as they became more pleasant and positive towards one another. Lisa realized she had now possessed all the tools she would need to be successful. The pathway would continue with self-awareness, self-love, and the ability to serve others.

However, Lisa would be adding to the way she served others and moving along in her healing process by using her voice. Sharing her voice required her to shed the "former more fearful Lisa." The process had not been easy, but she knew it was all worth it. Speaking engagements ensued, a new life of living whole began, and she felt better as a mom. Her children could now see the "whole" mom since the brokenness had healed. Lisa started advising women and young girls by sharing her experiences.

Some of her advice would be to "find your voice early," to "hold tightly to the voice once you've discovered it and to cultivate it." She would also advise to "ensure you keep your heart, mind, and soul focused on the right things," and "to remember that you live only one life so you must give it all you got."

Lisa also went on to advise the girls to "take the time needed to love yourself so you can love others," to "not rush life's precious moments," to "cherish family and friends," and to "give more than you receive." Each new day brought about a refreshing feeling, and Lisa was proud to say she was genuinely beginning to thrive and no longer just merely surviving. Feeling whole was no longer just a desire or something to hope for; it was real. Her hope had come to fruition. Lisa started to envision new goals for her new life. She was so excited and so thankful for the new journey. Lisa was soaring daily with every beautiful step she took toward her healing. Lisa had become the best version of Lisa that she had ever been.

Rediscover Me

When you awake daily, be willing to get to know me, discover me, ask me what makes me laugh, what makes me cry, my favorite movie.

The process of life will allow you to experience magical moments. The moments of discovery will enable you to peek into my soul. I'll gracefully touch your soul and ignite a flame that you must be present now to feel.

When the sun sets, and you take refuge to rest your body, sleep sound, and relax the body and soul. Prepare your space. Rediscover me daily, look into my eyes as if it's the first time, embrace me with a sensual and robust hug that represents protection and loyalty.

Touch me slowly and gracefully as if you are seeking for my most beautiful and sensitive spot.

Rediscover me over and over. Create and support a space of enjoyment that leads to satisfaction so deep that you will want to prepare for the next new experience immediately!

Discover my passion.

Rediscover my likes and dislikes as we live our best selves through the magical moment called LIFE. Rediscover me.

Meet me for the first time each day. I'll discover you, only to rediscover you daily.

Reviews

"Words cannot begin to describe how much she's helped me not only in my personal growth but my professional growth as well. Working with her allowed me to open a lot of deep wounds and address internal issues head on. She is patient, loving, and beyond supportive. She opened my eyes to things I did not realize I was internalizing (Grief, Self- Image, Relationships). There are no limitations to what she can address. Poetic Healer is a Savior!"

~Lace McGuire

Tina's Poetry is soothing to the soul

~Mo Mccarter

"Tea with Tina was a great event. It's not your normal Tea Party. She brings an amazing level of depth to the event. Tina is able to hold a space for those needing to explore and uncover some things. She allows you to be open, share, and relax within the space. I would definitely recommend!"

~Ka Rissa

"She is…Authentic, Uncut"

~Miche'l Denise

"I had an amazing time at Tea with Tina! Not only is she a gifted Poet, but she has such insight and a gift to help you explore emotions and begin to heal. I loved the safe, supportive, and fun space she created during Tea with Tina, so that us women could bond and share and rejoice in each cont. other. The tea and cupcakes were amazing too! Thank you for your spiritual gifts"

~Ellen Amis-Stilwell

"You will not regret reading something so real and authentic"

~Mary Thomas Jackson

"Her Platform allows others a safe space to express their selves"

~Sonda Jones Ward

"Time well spent is my first thought. I had a very pleasant afternoon among the very beautiful ladies in attendance. The interaction among the group was sun filled and interesting. The ideas shared were uplifting. Our Poetic Healer Story regarding her Tea With Tina endeavor was moving."

~Arlene McGuire

CPSIA information can be obtained
at www.ICGtesting.com
Printed in the USA
JSHW052015230920
8138JS00005B/27